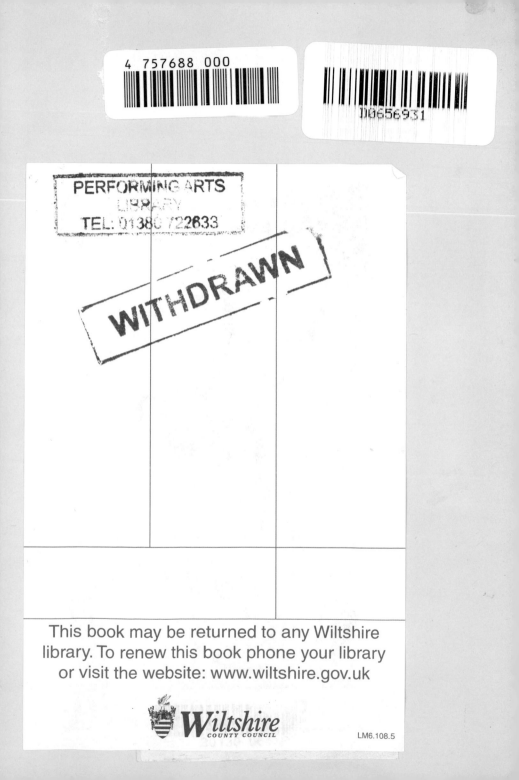

This book may be returned to any Wiltshire
library. To renew this book phone your library
or visit the website: www.wiltshire.gov.uk

Taking the Plunge

John Townsend

Stanley Thornes (Publishers) Ltd

Originally published in 1986 by Hutchinson Education
Reprinted 1986, 1988

Reprinted in 1990 by
Stanley Thornes (Publishers) Ltd
Old Station Drive
Leckhampton
CHELTENHAM GL53 0DN
England

Reprinted 1992

British Library Cataloguing in Publication Data

Townsend, John, 1924–
   Taking the plunge—(Spirals)
   1. Readers - 1950–
   I. Title   II. Series
   428.6′2   PE1121
ISBN 0 7487 0345 4

Printed and bound in Great Britain at
Martin's of Berwick

Contents

A complete list of Spirals

Stories

Jim Alderson
Crash in the Jungle
The Witch Princess

Jan Carew
Death Comes to the Circus

Susan Duberley
The Ring

**Keith Fletcher and
Susan Duberley**
Nightmare Lake

John Goodwin
Dead-end Job

Paul Groves
Not that I'm Work-shy
The Third Climber

Anita Jackson
The Actor
The Austin Seven
Bennet Manor
Dreams
The Ear
A Game of Life or Death
No Rent to Pay

Paul Jennings
Eye of Evil
Maggot

Margaret Loxton
The Dark Shadow

Patrick Nobes
Ghost Writer

Kevin Philbin
Summer of the Werewolf

John Townsend
Beware of the Morris Minor
Fame and Fortune
SOS

David Walke
Dollars in the Dust

Plays

Jan Carew
Computer Killer
No Entry
Time Loop

John Godfrey
When I Count to Three

Nigel Gray
An Earwig in the Ear

Paul Groves
Tell Me Where it Hurts

Barbara Mitchelhill
Punchlines
The Ramsbottoms at Home

Madeline Sotheby
Hard Times at Batwing Hall

John Townsend
Cheer and Groan
The End of the Line
Hanging by a Fred
The Lighthouse Keeper's Secret
Making a Splash
Murder at Muckleby Manor
Over and Out
Rocking the Boat
Taking the Plunge

David Walke
The Bungle Gang Strikes Again
The Good, the Bad and the Bungle
Package Holiday

A Body in the Attic

2 parts: Edna Plunge, Ted Plunge

Scene   A sitting room
Ted *is in an armchair.   He has his eyes shut.*

Edna   Are you awake, Ted?

   [*No reply*]

Edna   Ted?   Ted?   Are you asleep?

   [*No reply*]

Edna   Oi!   Ted.   Ted?   Ted!!

Ted   Eh?   What?   Er . . . did you say something, Edna?

Edna   Were you asleep?

Ted   No, course not.   I was just resting my eyes, why?

Edna   I just wondered.

Ted   Did you want something?

Edna   No.

Ted   Oh.   Are you sure?

Edna	Yes.
Ted	Oh.
Edna	It's just that . . .
Ted	What?
Edna	I fancy a cup of tea. Do you fancy a cup of tea?
Ted	Wouldn't mind.
Edna	Shall I put the kettle on?
Ted	Could do.
Edna	It will help to wake you up.
Ted	I am awake.
Edna	Oh, I thought you were asleep.
Ted	No, no. I was just looking at the inside of my eyelids for a few minutes.
Edna	Did you dream?
Ted	Pardon?
Edna	When you were asleep.
Ted	I told you, I was wide awake. You know I never sleep during the day. It keeps me awake at night.
Edna	But sleeping all night doesn't seem to keep you awake during the day.

6

Ted	I told you — I wasn't asleep just then.
Edna	Oh, I see. It's just that I thought you were.
Ted	What nonsense. You were quite wrong. What on earth gave you that idea, anyway?
Edna	You were snoring.
Ted	Weren't you going to put the kettle on?
Edna	Okay. [*She exits. Pause. She calls from the kitchen*] That's funny!
Ted	Pardon?
Edna	I said it's funny.
Ted	Is it? What?
Edna	[*Enters*] There's no water.
Ted	What do you mean? Didn't you turn the tap?
Edna	Of course I turned the tap. Nothing happened.
Ted	It must be the water people turning things off.
Edna	Well they didn't tell us. They usually let you know. Ooh, Ted, what if our pipes have burst somewhere?
Ted	Don't be daft, Edna. Pipes don't just crack. Besides, I would have heard it.

Edna	You were asleep.
Ted	Nonsense. Let me go and have a look. [*Exits. Pause*] You're right. Not a drip.
Edna	Go up in the loft, Ted.
Ted	Why?
Edna	It could be the ballcock.
Ted	Don't be silly, Edna.
Edna	It would put my mind at rest.
Ted	Don't fuss, Edna. You don't see me getting all worked up, do you dear? My mind is at rest.
Edna	That's because it's only just woken up.
Ted	Look — I've told you once . . . .
Edna	Do go up and have a look, Ted.
Ted	But what's the good of climbing up in the roof?
Edna	There might be a leak or a blockage or something. The tank might be dripping again. I would feel much better.
Ted	Then you know what to do. I always say there's nothing like a hot cup of tea to make you feel much better. That will do the trick.

Edna	Aren't you forgetting something?
Ted	Oh yes — and a biscuit. That always cheers you up. A custard cream with a nice hot cup of tea . . . .
Edna	How do I fill the kettle?
Ted	From the t. . . — ah, of course. I'm not very quick this afternoon, am I?
Edna	I'm not surprised. You've only just woken up.
Ted	Now, now, Edna. Don't start that nonsense again. I'm tired of telling you.
Edna	You shouldn't be tired of anything. You've only just woken up.
Ted	Look, Edna, will you stop keeping on about me falling asleep, not that I did, of course.
Edna	On one condition.
Ted	What's that?
Edna	You pop up to the loft.
Ted	Oh all right, if it keeps you happy. Can you find the torch? I'll fetch the ladder.
Edna	I knew you would see sense. I'll get your tool box, too. You never know what might need doing up there. I'll get you a duster and mop as well. It's bound to need a

spring clean up there while you're about it. We haven't been up in that attic for ages, not since er . . . when was it?

Ted   Not since the plumber came last time to mend the tank. [*On the landing*] Hold the ladder steady, Edna. It's a bit wobbly. I don't think it's on level ground.

Edna   No, it's on my slipper.

Ted   Hang on. The trap door is a bit stiff. The latch is a bit bent.

Edna   So is my slipper.

Ted   Ah, it's all right, that's better. I've opened it. Ooh, you're right — it is a bit dusty up here.

Edna   Don't forget to wash your hands when you come down.

Ted   I'll just have a look round. I must be careful where I tread. I mustn't go through the floorboards.

Edna   Can you see anything?

Ted   Not yet.

Edna   Can you hear any drips?

Ted   Not yet.

Edna   Can you find the problem?

Ted	Not yet. BLIMEY!
Edna	Got it?
Ted	Cor, Gordon Bennet! Love a duck!
Edna	Found it?
Ted	Strike a light! Heavens above! Crikey! Good grief! Crumbs!
Edna	Seen it?
Ted	Flipping heck!
Edna	Done it?
Ted	Blooming blazes!
Edna	Solved it?
Ted	Stone the crows! Blow me sideways!
Edna	Something there?
Ted	Just fancy! Who'd have thought it?
Edna	What's up?

[Pause]

Edna	Ted? Have you found what it is?

[Pause]

Edna	Are you there? What is it? Ted?

Ted	Blimey, Edna. I've unblocked it all right. I've found it good and proper.
Edna	Great! Ted, you're wonderful. What was it?
Ted	Er um a . . .
Edna	What was that?
Ted	It's a er um er . . .
Edna	Spit it out, dear. What was the trouble?
Ted	A body.
Edna	Oh no. It wasn't a mouse or anything horrid was it?
Ted	Not quite, dear.
Edna	. . . or a sparrow in the tank again?
Ted	Not exactly, Edna.
Edna	What then?
Ted	There's a dead man up here, Edna.
Edna	Are you sure?
Ted	Yes.
Edna	Are you certain?
Ted	Yes.
Edna	You're not mistaken?

Ted	Edna, I know a corpse when I see one. I tell you, I have just found a dead man up here in the attic.
Edna	Is it anyone we know?
Ted	I can't be sure. He does look a bit familiar.
Edna	Which bit?
Ted	He's got something in his hand.
Edna	What on earth will they say next door when I tell them? How do you know he's not asleep?
Ted	Don't be absurd. I can tell when someone is asleep, you know.
Edna	You couldn't this afternoon downstairs. Are you sure he isn't snoring like you were?
Ted	Don't be daft. He is certainly not breathing.
Edna	How can you be sure?
Ted	Because his head is two feet under water. He is slumped in the water tank.
Edna	Shall I phone the plumber?
Ted	Don't talk such rubbish, Edna.
Edna	Why?

Ted	It *is* the plumber. I remember who it is now. He's still got the plunger in his hand.
Edna	What do you mean?
Ted	You know when we had trouble with the tank before and we sent for the plumber?
Edna	Yes.
Ted	Do you remember him leaving?
Edna	Now you come to mention it − no!
Ted	You didn't see him go?
Edna	No.
Ted	He must have kicked the bucket on the job. How awful. This is dreadful.
Edna	Thank goodness we hadn't paid him yet. Lucky he managed to finish it before er . . . well, before he passed on.
Ted	When was the last time you saw him?
Edna	I brought him up a cup of tea. I just put my head through the trap door and . . . yes, I remember now. He was asleep so I didn't want to disturb him. He looked so peaceful.
Ted	The man was dead, Edna. Didn't you know a dead man when you saw one? Can't you tell if a man is asleep or not?

Edna	With you I can, like this afternoon. I thought he was just resting his eyes like you do sometimes.
Ted	What, underwater? You can always tell when I'm asleep, can't you? Surely you can tell the difference?
Edna	But you're always dropping off.
Ted	Nonsense — aaaah! [*CRASH!*]
Edna	What was that?
Ted	I've just dropped off! My foot has gone through the floorboards. My slipper has fallen down to our bedroom.
Edna	Shall I phone the police or something?
Ted	No, it's all right — I'll get it back myself.
Edna	No, no, about the plumber. We had better tell someone. There might be a lot of people still waiting for him to unblock their sinks.
Ted	I think you'd better phone. While you're about it, get someone to come and get me out. I'm stuck. My leg is trapped down the hole.
Edna	Who shall I phone?
Ted	Look in the Yellow Pages.

Edna   What shall I look under? Dead plumbers?
          I'd better dial 999. You'll stay there, won't
          you? Is the plumber all right?

Ted   He doesn't look too bad. I sat him in that
          old rocking chair up here — the one with
          woodworm. He looks quite comfortable,
          with the plunger still in his hand. He seems
          fine — dead, but fine. Go on, you phone
          the police. We'll be all right up here. I'll
          probably have another little nap. I could do
          with a little rest again. After all this, I'm
          feeling dead tired.

Edna   I'll put the kettle on. We'll all feel much
          better after a nice cup of tea — I'm not
          sure about the plumber though. Such a nice
          chap. The last thing he said to me was that
          he hoped to drop in sometime soon. What
          a shame. I told you our water was different
          lately. It seemed to have more body in it.
          He was a good plumber. He really got into
          his job. Anyway, I'm glad we've found what
          was blocking the water pipes. It could have
          been serious. I nearly had to boil some milk
          for coffee and it just wouldn't be the same
          as a nice cup of tea. Now where did I put
          that kettle? [Exits]

16

A Bit of a Mix-up

3 parts: Edna Plunge, Policeman, Mrs Plum (rather posh)

Scene   A telephone conversation

Edna   [*On the phone*] Hello. Hello?

   [*Pause*]

Edna   Hello? Hello?

Police   Hello?

Edna   Hello.

Police   Police here — hello, hello, hello?

Edna   I'm sorry, I can't hear too well. It's not a very good line. Hello?

Police   Hello? Speak up, please. It's not a very good line. Hello?

Edna   Pardon? Hello, are you there?

Police   Hello? Hello? Speak up please, can you hear me? What's your message?

Edna   Yes, it is mild today, isn't it?

Police	I beg your pardon? Please report your message.
Edna	Oh, oh, I see. Yes, I would like to report a dead plumber.
Police	A wet summer? Yes it has been, but please report your message. Please speak up.
Edna	A wet summer? Yes, but it's mild today, don't you think? In fact I was saying to Ted only this morning about it.
Police	About it? About what? What do you mean? Will you please speak up and report your message. It's a bad line.
Edna	There is a dead plumber in our attic.
Police	What's he doing up there?
Edna	Nothing. Nothing at all. He died, you see.
Police	Oh dear. I'm so sorry to hear that. Was it something serious?
Edna	He drowned.
Police	By mistake?
Edna	Oh yes, he didn't mean to. The poor man must have splashed around up there for hours. Just think of the mess.
Police	What? You'll have to shout.

Edna	[*Shouting*] He's sitting in a rocking chair now — holding a plunger.
Police	Sorry, it must be the line. I thought you said he was sitting in a rocking chair holding a plunger. This line is very bad. I can hear other voices.
Mrs Plum	Hello? Hello? Is that the Sink-Tank Company?
Police	I beg your pardon?
Edna	I beg your pardon? Who?
Mrs P.	The plumber. I must have a plumber.
Edna	But I've told you — he's dead.
Police	Are you reporting a murder?
Mrs. P.	Good heavens man, no — just a blockage. The drains.
Police	Sorry, I think we've got a crossed line.
Mrs P.	No, not a line, a pipe. It's the drains.
Edna	Pardon? Did you say trains? I thought you were the police station, not the railway station.
Police	Where are you?
Edna	My name is Edna Plunge and we live at thirty-two Peabody Drive and the plumber is in the roof.

Police	On the roof?
Mrs P.	On the roof?
Edna	Why are you repeating yourself?
Mrs P.	I'm not.
Police	I'm not.
Edna	Who is that?
Police	Who is that?
Mrs P.	Who is that?
Edna	I think it's a crossed line.
Police	You can say that again. No, on second thoughts I'd rather you didn't.
Mrs P.	But I'm phoning up for a plumber. It's urgent. There's water running down the walls. The whole thing is quite beastly.
Police	I'm sorry, I can't really help you. I deal with matters of life and death.
Mrs P.	This is a matter of life and death. It's my 'U'-bend.
Police	Gosh. I see what you mean.
Mrs P.	I want the Sink-Tank Company but we were cut off. They just went dead on the line.
Police	Dead on the line? Were they hit by a train?

20

Edna.	Is that the railway station again? You've got to come. My husband is stuck in the roof with a dead plumber with a plunger still in his hand. He put him in the rocking chair, the plumber that is — with woodworm.
Mrs P.	A plumber with woodworm?
Edna	I'm sorry, you'll have to speak up. I think we're having a bit of a mix-up.
Mrs P.	You're telling me.
Police	You're telling me.
Edna	Now you're repeating again.
Mrs P.	Repeating?
Police	Repeating? It's not me.
Mrs P.	Well it's not me. Help! Something has burst! The water is up to my ankles. Please send the plumber.
Edna	But he's dead.
Mrs P.	It doesn't matter. It's better than nothing.
Police	Just try to calm down, madam. Now I'm trying to write all this down in my notebook. Please tell me again clearly. Try to speak up. The line is crackling again.
Edna	Yes. I would like to report a dead body in the attic. It started when I wanted a nice cup of tea. I couldn't get any water.

Mrs P.	You can have some of mine. It's up to my knees! It's beastly!
Police	Sorry, I didn't quite catch that.
Edna	My husband went up to the attic. He is Ted.
Police	Your husband is dead?
Edna	Pardon?
Police	Is your husband the plumber?
Mrs P.	Oh, if he is, send him round. It's up to my waist.
Edna	. . . and he found the body. Can you send someone to carry him away?
Police	Your husband?
Edna	The plumber.
Mrs P.	Hello? Hello? Did you say you're the plumber? You've got to help me before I drown.
Police	Did you say drown?
Edna	Well he could have drowned, we're not sure. He was slumped in the tank upside down.
Mrs P.	The tank is upside down? Then come and put it the right way up.
Edna	My husband fell and he's stuck up there with him.

Police	Let me get this clear. Who's dead?
Edna	Who's 'l'ed? I told you, my husband.
Police	I'm very sorry to hear that, madam. Let me have your address.
Mrs P.	Sixty-eight, The Green . . .
Edna	Thirty-two, Peabody Drive . . .
Mrs P.	at the top of the hill . . .
Edna	on the corner . . .
Mrs P.	by the post office . . .
Edna	over the road from the park . . .
Mrs P.	Have you got that? It's up to my chest, help! How beastly!
Police	Could I have your name?
Edna	Plunge. The name is Edna Plunge.
Mrs P.	Plum. The name is Mrs Plum.
Police	Make up your mind.
Mrs P.	I'm going to swim for it. It's up to my neck.
Police	Where are you going?
Mrs P.	For the plumber. Where did you say he was?
Edna	Thirty-two, Peabody Drive.

Police	Thirty-two, Peabody Drive?
Mrs P.	I'll be round. Help!
Edna	Hello? Hello?
Police	Hello? Where are those bubbles coming from? I'll have to come round. This line is getting worse. Now let me get this right . . .
Edna	Hello, hello? Is anyone there?
Police	I'll just read back what I've got in my notebook. The name is Plunge, you have a dead husband with woodworm, slumped in a cup of tea, stuck to a plunger in a rocking chair and the plumber hit the roof and you're in it up to your neck. You live at sixty-eight Peabody Green over the hill at the top of the post office. . . .
Edna	Hello? Hello? I can't hear you.
Police	This sounds like a serious crime. You must have killed him. Was it revenge?
Edna	No, Plunge. Edna and Ted. I've already given you my name. We're at thirty-two Peabody Drive and my husband has lost his slipper.
Police	Sorry? Did you say he lost his temper? Was it GBH?

Edna	No, from Marks & Spencer. His slipper just went.
Police	Are you saying it was stolen?
Edna	Good heavens, no. It's on our bed. It fell through the ceiling when he dropped off.
Police	He's in bed and he dropped off? So he's asleep and not dead after all? This seems very odd to me. One minute he's dead and the next he's asleep. I'd better come round right away and sort this thing out.
Edna	Oh good. I'll put the kettle on. Do you take sugar?
Police	Pardon? I can't hear you. Did you say you're at number thirty-two?
Edna	No, I said how many sugars do you take?
Police	Thirty-two?
Edna	Blimey, that's half a packet!
Police	What about the undertaker?
Edna	He may not take sugar.
Police	He'll have to come round and measure the body. Can you say how long he might be?
Edna	He could take ages.
Police	No, I mean about how high is the body?

Edna	Only a few centimetres — he's lying down.
Police	Hello?
Edna	The line has gone dead.
Police	Hello? Hello? Hello?
Edna	He must have gone. I don't know what things are coming to. Policemen today are rather odd. He said water was up to his chest and he could hear bubbles. I must have caught him in the bath. He must have had soap in his ears because he didn't catch half of what I said. People just don't listen these days. They do get things mixed up. I can't think why. After all, I made it all quite clear. I'm glad we're on the phone. Where would we be without it? I feel really thirsty after all that. [*Puts phone down*] How about a nice cup of tea? Now then, where did I put that kettle? [*Exits*]

A Plum in the Mouth

4 parts: Edna Plunge, Ted Plunge, Mrs Plum (rather posh), Policeman

Scene   Edna and Ted's house

Edna   [Calling up from the landing] Ted! Are you there?

[No reply]

Edna   Ted! Can you hear me?

[No reply]

Edna   Oi! Ted! Are you asleep in the attic? Ted!!!

Ted   Eh, er, what? Did you say something, Edna?

Edna   He's coming round.

Ted   He can't, he's dead.

Edna   Pardon?

Ted   The plumber. Don't you remember? He's up here with me in the attic. He won't come round. He'll never get better now. He's well and truly dead.

Edna	No, the policeman. I've just phoned the police. He'll be round soon to take the body away.
Ted	I hope he'll get me out while he's about it. I'm still stuck, you know. I've fallen through to my waist. There's a big hole in our bedroom ceiling. I'm well and truly trapped.
Edna	I know, dear. I went in and saw your legs hanging down over our bed. I told you not to wear those socks. They're old ones. [Doorbell] Ah, here he is. [Exits]
Ted	At last! Bring him straight up. I'm getting cramp. It's very dark and dusty up here. What a place for the plumber to choose to kick the bucket. I wonder how long he's been up here − just floating in our water tank. At least he's more comfortable now. I knew that old rocking chair would come in handy sometime. He looks quite peaceful sitting there with the plunger in his hand.
Edna	Ted? Cooee, it's not the policeman, it's a lady. [In a whisper] She's rather posh. [Calling downstairs] If you'd like to come up Mrs er um, what was the name?
Mrs Plum	Plum.
Edna	I beg your pardon?

Mrs P.	Plum. Mrs Plum — as in fruit.
Edna	We're Plunge. Ted and Edna Plunge, as in splash.
Mrs P.	I know, I heard you on the phone.
Edna	You're very wet.
Mrs P.	My house is flooded. I must have the plumber. It's beastly.
Ted	Who is it?
Edna	Mrs Pear and she's very wet.
Mrs P.	Plum.
Edna	Pardon?
Mrs P.	The name is Plum.
Ted	I can't hear you down there.
Mrs P.	We had crossed lines on the phone. You said you've got a plumber here. I've got a burst pipe — so beastly, you know. I heard the plumber is in the attic. I need him quickly.
Ted	Who is it and what do they want?
Mrs P.	[*Calling up to him*] Where's the plumber?
Ted	He's sitting up here in a rocking chair.

Mrs P.	How shocking. He can't sit down and rest at a time like this. I need him straightaway. It's so beastly.
Ted	What's the rush? Have you come to take him away right now?
Mrs P.	Yes, of course. Tell him it's urgent.
Edna	I don't think he'll understand.
Mrs P.	Isn't he English, then?
Edna	I don't think you understand, Mrs Peach, you see . . .
Mrs P.	Plum! Look, can't he come back to you when he's finished at my house? I'll pay him extra. I'm in a beastly mess.
Ted	You'll have to come up and get him.
Mrs P.	Don't be so daft.

[Doorbell]

Edna	Oh, that must be the police.
Ted	Pardon? Who's there? What's going on?
Mrs P.	Police?
Edna	I won't be a moment. How many sugars, Mrs Melon?
Mrs P.	Plum. What?

Edna	Sugar.
Mrs P.	What's that got to do with it?
Edna	I'm going to put the kettle on. [*Exits*]
Mrs P.	I haven't got time for that. I'm a busy lady, you know. Now then, are you going to come down from up there or not?
Ted	I can't. I'm stuck.
Mrs P.	How beastly. But I'm not so worried about you — what about the plumber?
Ted	You'll have to carry him. He's flat out.
Mrs P.	Are you telling me the man is drunk? This is beastly. I only need him for an hour then you can have him back again.
Ted	What on earth for? We've had him long enough as it is. He's been here for two months.
Mrs P.	He'll charge the earth for that long. What's he been doing?
Ted	Just leaning over the tank.
Mrs P.	Not very nice for him. He must be a little stiff by now.
Ted	No, not really. Quite floppy, in fact.
Edna	He's up here, officer. Do come up.

Police	I think I had better check all the facts. I'm not too sure about some of them. My notebook is in a muddle.
Mrs P.	What's this policeman doing here?
Police	Good afternoon, madam. It's Mrs Apple, isn't it?
Mrs P.	Plum. How do you know me?
Edna	I told him.
Police	She told me. Besides, I remember you. You reported a crime last year. Robbery, wasn't it?
Mrs P.	Yes. It was all so beastly. Haven't you caught him yet? It's high time you did.
Police	Er, not yet, madam.
Mrs P.	We pay you policemen all that money to find thieves and you never seem to catch them. I gave you a very clear picture of the man who robbed my house.
Police	We're doing our best, Mrs Cherry.
Mrs P.	Plum. I will never forget his face — so beastly.
Ted	Who is it down there? This roof won't hold out much longer. I'm trapped and slipping down further. Quick!

Edna	That's my husband. He's stuck in the roof.
Mrs P.	What about the plumber?
Edna	Oh, he's just sitting up there in the rocking chair — with woodworm.
Police	You'll need to phone the doctor for that.
Edna	Can they cure woodworm these days?
Police	No. A doctor has to sign all the forms to say how he died.
Mrs P.	How he died? What is all this?
Police	Yes, madam, how he died.
Ted	Hurry up!
Edna	We think he drowned.
Mrs P.	Drowned?
Edna	Yes, Mrs Gooseberry.
Mrs P.	Plum. I don't follow all this. I feel muddled.
Edna	You need a nice hot cup of tea. Shall I put the kettle on?
Police	I think we'd better get the body down first. I'll just climb up the steps. My word, it's rather dark up here.
Ted	Quick! I'm starting to slip right through.

Edna	Just sit down a while, Mrs Lemon. It's been a nasty shock.
Mrs P.	Plum. Of course it has. My house is flooded. I need a plumber. I've got a beastly blockage.
Edna	Well I'm phoning the doctor in a moment. I'll ask him to see you.
Mrs P.	Not me, my drains. It's my sink, I think.
Edna	Have you got a plunger?
Mrs P.	Don't be so daft!
Edna	The plumber has got one. It won't be any good to him now. You're welcome to use it if we can get him down. Are you all right up there?
Police	Just about, madam. I'm lifting the plumber down to you. He's dead heavy.
Ted	Quick! You'd better leave him and help me for a moment. I'm slipping through this hole.
Police	Of course, sir. I'll leave the plumber at the top of the ladder.
Edna	Ah, here he comes. Look, there's the plumber looking down at us. Bless him, doesn't he look sweet? At least he's at peace.

Mrs P.	He doesn't look too well to me. He's very wrinkled.
Edna	Of course. He's been under water for weeks.
Mrs P.	It can't have done him much good. He looks so pale and floppy. Why isn't he moving? He's just staring at us. I say, how rude! He's sticking his tongue out at me.
Edna	But we've told you, he's . . .
Mrs P.	What?
Edna	He's passed on.
Mrs P.	How do you mean?
Edna	He's been taken from us.
Mrs P.	What are you getting at?
Edna	He's been called above.
Mrs P.	I know. He's in the attic.
Edna	He's six feet under.
Mrs P.	He can't be. He's above our heads.
Edna	What I'm trying to say is, he's met his maker, kicked the bucket, snuffed it, pegged out, breathed his last, passed away . . . GONE! In other words, he dropped dead.

Mrs P.	Aaaaaah! How beastly. [*She faints*]
Police	What was that down there? It's no good, sir, I can't keep hold of you much longer. Something is starting to give.
Ted	The floor?
Police	No, my trousers!
Ted	You'll have to . . . aaaaaah! [*He falls through the floor*]
Police	Blimey — he's gone! What's worse, he's taken my trousers with him!
Edna	What's happened? There's an awful lot of dust down here. Oh dear, Mrs Orange has fainted.
Ted	Eeh, that's better. I feel much happier now. This bed is just the job. Who put the lights out?
Police	I'm afraid I'm stuck, madam. I've just put my foot through the floorboards. Your husband has fallen right down to your bed. He seems all right, except he's got my trousers over his head.
Ted	It's pitch black down here. Am I dead? Did I kill myself?
Edna	I think Mrs Raspberry is beginning to come round.

Police	Pardon?
Edna	She's coming round.
Police	But I thought she was already here.
Edna	Poor woman, she had a shock. She's waking up.
Police	I'm sorry about your ceiling. It's full of holes. The plumber is hanging upside down out of the trap door. It's lucky his plunger has sucked onto the rafters.
Edna	He's just staring down at us with his mouth wide open.
Mrs P.	Where am I? I feel quite beastly.
Edna	Thirty-two Peabody Drive. Plunge. My name is Edna Plunge. There is a policeman stuck in the loft in his underwear, a dead plumber above our heads, upside down and swinging from a plunger, and my husband is asleep on the bed after falling through the ceiling, wearing trousers on his head. Do you remember now? Everything is quite normal, there's nothing at all to worry about. It's all right now. I'll just put the kettle on for a nice cup of tea. [*Exits*]
Mrs P.	This must be a dream. Aaah! There it is again. It's staring down at me. Help! Police! It's him.

Police	Who? What's the matter, Mrs Prune?
Mrs P.	Plum. The thief — the one who broke into my house. He's up there with his eyes and mouth wide open.
Police	Are you sure, Mrs Banana?
Mrs P.	Plum. Of course, I can tell when a mouth is shut or not.
Police	No, I mean are you quite sure it's the crook?
Mrs. P.	He's the one. He robbed me. It's his beastly face. He said he was the plumber and got into my house and stole all my silver.
Police	So that was his game. He's got a bag up here, too. What's he got in it? I can see silver in my torchlight. Yes, silver and gold. The crook has been caught!
Mrs P.	I hope he gets locked up for life. He mustn't escape. They mustn't let him get away.
Police	I don't think there's any chance of that from where he's going. It's a one-way ticket. I expect he was up to the same tricks round here. He was robbing the Plunges. He must have pegged out on the job. His nerve finally snapped.

Edna	[*Enters with tray*] Like your trousers. Tea, Mrs Grape?
Mrs P.	Plum. Do you know, I'm glad I came round here this afternoon.
Edna	You're welcome. We have a cuppa most afternoons.
Mrs P.	No, no. The plumber isn't a plumber. He's a burglar.
Edna	Then what was he doing in our water tank?
Police	He was probably having a wash.
Edna	Having a wash?
Police	So he could make a clean get-away! We've caught him red-handed.
Edna	But what would a crook be doing right up there in the roof?
Police	Looking for things of higher quality! He must be at the top of his career! He's a cat burglar.
Edna	What would he want to steal our Tiddles for?
Mrs P.	Aaaah! I think he just moved. How ever so horrid and beastly. Yes, it's him all right. I would know him anywhere. His mouth is a bit different but apart from that, he's just the same. It's quite beastly. [*Sips tea*]

Edna	He hasn't got any teeth in. That's why he looks different.
Mrs P.	Er! What's this? Aaaah! I've got them! I've got his teeth. They're in my cup of tea! How did they get there?
Edna	Oh dear! They must have come through the tap. After all, he has been upside down in our water tank for a long time.
Mrs P.	I think I'm going to faint again. To think, I almost swallowed a dead man's teeth. It doesn't bear thinking about. How beastly. Whatever would I have done?
Edna	Oh it's all right. The dentist would have made him a new set.
Police	I don't like to alarm anyone but the floorboards up here are creaking like mad. The plumber is slipping, too. His plunger is giving way. My legs have slipped right through into the bedroom.
Mrs P.	I feel quite dizzy. Aaah! How beastly! Look! The policeman's legs! He's got no trousers. I'm going to faint.
Edna	Have a nice hot cup of tea, Mrs Greengage.
Mrs P.	It is Plum. The name is Plum and that is all. It's not Apple, not Banana, not Pear, not a whole blooming fruit salad, but pure

and simple PLUM! PLUM, PLUM, PLUM, PLUM, PLUM. I hope that's clear. [*She faints*]

Police   Is she all right down there? She does sound rather odd.

Edna   These posh people do tend to speak with plums in their mouths. She's just upset, that's all. Poor lady is in a bit of a state at home. Mrs Plum is flooded out.

Police   She's a damson in distress! You could get a reward, you know.

Edna   What, for making her faint again?

Police   For stopping a thief. He was caught red-handed. We've been after him for years. Eek! What was that? Oh no, it's giving way . . . aaaaaaaaah! [*He falls through*]

Edna   Are you all right?

Ted   Good afternoon, officer. So nice of you to drop in. Would you like your trousers back?

Police   So sorry to disturb your sleep, Mr Plunge.

Ted   Strike a light! The whole blooming ceiling has fallen down!

Police   And our friend the plumber has landed between the ladies.

Edna   Sugar, Mrs Plum?

Mrs P.	Aaah, I've got the rest of the plumber in my cup of tea now!
Edna	One lump or two? Oh good, he's got his teeth back. Oh no, what's that hissing noise?
Mrs P.	I know that noise! I've been hearing it in my house all afternoon. It's beastly. It's water, running water. It's flying everywhere – help! All this water, I hate it. You know how it makes me feel, don't you?
All	BEASTLY?
Mrs P.	No, wet!
Ted	The tank has burst.
Mrs P.	Phone the plumber.
Police	Phone the doctor.
Ted	Phone the undertaker.
Police	Phone the police!
Edna	Phone the builder – but before I do, there is one thing I must see to.
Mrs P.	What?
Police	What?
Ted	What?

Edna   I must warm the pot. Who's for a nice cup of hot tea? Now where did I put that kettle?